Contents

MUTINY ON HALYCRUS

Characters

Scott

Thirteen-year-old Scott's favourite things are science and skateboarding – and avoiding his snoopy big sister.

AJ

Scott's daredevil friend AJ is always taking crazy risks, and he has lots of cuts and bruises to show for it.

Rudy

The conscience of the group. He likes woodwork, hanging with Scott and AJ, and his Red Sox cap.

Penny

Scott's fourteen-year-old sister Penny likes to poke her nose into his life – and get him into trouble.

Halycrusians

Inhabitants of the environmentally ravaged planet Halycrus. They live underground, hiding from the vicious mountain swine.

Z-kee

T-kwinia

R-cher

Out of this World

MUTINY ON HALYCRUS

by Keira Wong

illustrated by Douglas Fong

H A L Y C R U S

All rights reserved.
This 2009 edition published in the United Kingdom by
Scholastic Ltd
Villiers House
Clarendon Avenue
Leamington Spa
Warwickshire
CV32 5PR

First published in 2007
by Macmillan Education Australia Pty Ltd.

Copyright © 2007 Laguna Bay Publishing Pty Ltd.
www.lagunabaypublishing.com

Text by Keira Wong
Illustrations by Douglas Fong
Cover Design Allison Parry
Designed by Matt Lin/Goblin Design
Managing Editor Nicola Robinson

Out of this World: Mutiny on Halycrus
ISBN 978 1407 10104 0

Printed by Tien Wah Press, Singapore

1 2 3 4 5 6 7 8 9   9 0 1 2 3 4 5 6 7 8

H A L Y C R U S

SCOTT, RUDY AND AJ ARE HELPING THEIR HALYCRUSIAN FRIENDS MOVE TO A SAFE NEW ISLAND HOME. THE ISLAND IS COVERED IN BEJAIS - JEWEL-LIKE BAUBLES WHICH ARE THE HALYCRUSIANS' ONLY FOOD - AND IS FREE FROM THE VICIOUS MOUNTAIN SWINE.

NO MOUNTAIN SWINE ... Z-KEE, IS THIS TRUE?

IT IS! WELCOME TO BEJAIS ISLAND! MY ONLY CONCERN IS THERE'S NO SHELTER.

IF THERE'S NO SWINE, WE DON'T NEED ANY SHELTER!

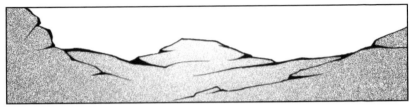

YOU'RE RIGHT, T-KWINIA. I CAN FORGET MY OLD FEARS!

WHO'S LEFT AT THE CAVE CITY?

ALAS, SCOTT, R-CHER AND HIS FRIENDS PREFER TO TAKE THEIR CHANCES WITH THE SWINE.

MEANWHILE, R-CHER HAS PLANS FOR THE EMPTY CAVE CITY.

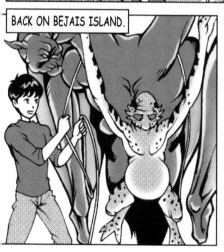

BACK ON BEJAIS ISLAND.

OUCH! THE ROPE VINE SCRATCHES!

IT'S THE ONLY WAY THE WINGED TWO-HEADS CAN CARRY YOU.

BUT IT'S VERY UNCOMFORTABLE.

MAYBE WE CAN FIND ANOTHER WAY.

YES! WE'LL LOOK IN MY DAD'S GARAGE!

C'MON! LET'S GET BACK TO THE CAVE CITY.

AND THEN BACK TO EARTH.

- 7 -

BACK ON EARTH, THE BOYS HUNT THROUGH THE BOTCHED COURIER DELIVERIES THAT SCOTT'S DAD STORES IN THE GARAGE.

THIS IS A GOLD MINE, SCOTT!

HEY! THESE LOOK NICE AND SOFT!

THAT WAS THE BALLET SCHOOL'S EXTRA ORDER. THEY'RE PERFECT!

NICE SCARF, AJ! MATCHES YOUR EYES!

HUH? SOUNDS LIKE SCOTT AND HIS FRIENDS ARE UP TO SOMETHING ...

UNFORTUNATELY, SCOTT'S SISTER PENNY IS LISTENING AT THE DOOR.

WE'LL GO THROUGH THE PORTAL TONIGHT.

PORTAL? WHAT? THAT'S IT, I'M FOLLOWING SCOTT TONIGHT.

THAT NIGHT THE BOYS SKATE DOWN TO THE LOCAL SCRAPYARD – AND THE ROCK THAT BECOMES THE PORTAL TO ANOTHER PLANET …

ALL PORTALS LEAD TO HALYCRUS! READY, GUYS?

GO FOR IT!

MEANWHILE, BEHIND A TREE …

JUST WHAT ARE THEY UP TO?

SPLAT!

ONE OF SCOTT'S SCHOOL SCIENCE EXPERIMENTS TURNED OUT TO BE A PORTAL MIXTURE ...

THE MIXTURE CONTAINS SOME OF HIS SISTER'S EYE MAKE-UP AND IS ACTIVATED WHEN HURLED AT THE ROCK.

SEE YOU ON THE OTHER SIDE!

HIS LEG HAS DISAPPEARED!!!!

AFTER YOU, KIND SIR.

WHY THANK YOU.

AJ AND RUDY HAVE DISAPPEARED AS WELL!!!

SO THEY TOUCHED THIS SHINING STUFF?

MEANWHILE, IN THE CAVE CITY THERE IS SOME EXCITEMENT ...

THE ONLY WEAPON THAT WORKS AGAINST THE SWINE IS SOFT DRINK. IT BURNS THEIR HAIR.

SCOTT, WHERE ARE WE?

I'LL TAKE PENNY DOWN TO THE CAVE CITY. GO AND BURN SWINE!

PENNY, GO WITH RUDY. I'LL EXPLAIN EVERYTHING LATER.

I WANT TO GO HOME!

HOLD ON, AJ!

DON'T WORRY, PENNY. IT'S OK.

RUDY HELPS PENNY DOWN THE TUNNEL TO SAFETY ...

... AND FINDS SOMEWHERE FOR HER TO SIT AND CALM DOWN SO HE CAN EXPLAIN THE SITUATION.

EAT THIS, PENNY. THIS IS HALYCRUSIAN FOOD: A BEJAIS.

IT'LL MAKE YOU FEEL A LOT BETTER, I PROMISE!

I DON'T WANT TO EAT ANYTHING!

A FEMALE HALYCRUSIAN APPROACHES THE KIDS.

RUDY, SCOTT WANTS YOU ABOVE GROUND.

STAY HERE. I'M JUST GOING TO SEE SCOTT.

I'LL SHOW YOU THE WAY BACK TO EARTH, HUMAN GIRL. FOLLOW ME.

HOME?

SCOTT AND AJ CELEBRATE VICTORY OVER THE SWINE.

YEA-AH! GOOD ONE!

WELL DONE! BUT WHAT DID YOU CALL ME UP FOR?

WE DIDN'T.

BUT—

IS PENNY OK? DON'T TRY TO MIND-READ WITH HER. IT'LL BE TOO CONFUSING.

OK. BUT I'VE EXPLAINED THE WHOLE STORY TO HER.

WE'RE USED TO IT! IMAGINE HOW HARD IT MUST BE FOR PENNY!

GERAGHH!

GERAGHH!

SCOTT! AJ! WE NEED SOME HELP.

UDY IS FORCED DOWN THE TUNNEL.

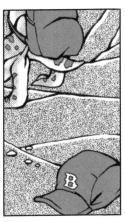

SCOTT, AJ AND Z-KEE ARRIVE, ONLY TO FIND RUDY AND PENNY MISSING.

WHERE'S PENNY? WHERE'S RUDY?

R-CHER'S FRIEND Q-STER PRETENDS TO HELP.

THEY RETURNED TO EARTH.

WHY? RUDY KNEW WE WERE ALL GOING TO GO HOME TOGETHER. ANYWAY, I HAVE THE PORTAL MIXTURES.

SPEAK THE TRUTH, Q-STER!

I AM. BUT THE ONLY ORDERS I LISTEN TO COME FROM R-CHER. NOT YOU, Z-KEE!

AJ AND SCOTT BLOCK THEIR PRIVATE THOUGHTS FROM Q-STER.

LOOK!

RUDY'S CAP! BUT HE NEVER TAKES THAT OFF!

Q-STER, WAIT ...

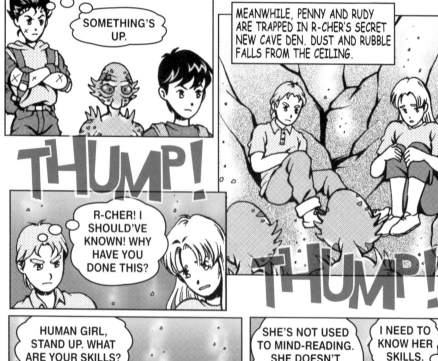

SOMETHING'S UP.

MEANWHILE, PENNY AND RUDY ARE TRAPPED IN R-CHER'S SECRET NEW CAVE DEN. DUST AND RUBBLE FALLS FROM THE CEILING.

THUMP!

R-CHER! I SHOULD'VE KNOWN! WHY HAVE YOU DONE THIS?

THUMP!

HUMAN GIRL, STAND UP. WHAT ARE YOUR SKILLS?

SHE'S NOT USED TO MIND-READING. SHE DOESN'T UNDERSTAND YOUR WAY OF COMMUNICATING!

I NEED TO KNOW HER SKILLS.

YOU HUMANS HAVE ALWAYS PROVED TO BE USEFUL.

THUMP!

YOUR EARTH TROLLEYS COLLECT BEJAIS QUICKLY. YOUR EARTH SOFT DRINK BURNS THE SWINES' HAIR!

IF YOU STAYED HERE ALL THE TIME YOU'D BE USEFUL ALL THE TIME. AND THE MORE OF YOU THE BETTER!

WHY DO I HEAR ALL THESE VOICES IN MY HEAD? IT'S MAKING ME FEEL SICK!

I FOLLOWED SCOTT BECAUSE I THOUGHT HE WAS SKATING IN THE PARK IN THE MIDDLE OF THE NIGHT.

IT'S OK. SCOTT WILL BE HERE SOON.

RUDY KNOWS THE BEJAIS SUPPLY ENERGY, EVEN TO HUMANS.

BUT HE'S HERE IN A LAND OF MONSTERS!

COME ON. IT'LL MAKE YOU FEEL BETTER.

THUMP!

GIVE ME THAT BEJAIS! NO FOOD FOR YOU!

I DON'T WANT THEM TO HAVE THE ENERGY TO ESCAPE!

THUMP!

HERE'S THE WOOD YOU BROUGHT FROM EARTH.

THUMP!

MAKE THE TROLLEYS YOU WERE GOING TO TEACH US TO MAKE. HA!

I DON'T HAVE THE ENERGY.

RUDY TRIES TO KEEP HIS THOUGHTS PRIVATE.

HE'LL HAVE TO GIVE ME A BEJAIS IF HE WANTS ME TO WORK. THEN I'LL RUN!

SLAP!

- 20 -

MY FRIEND, WHEN YOU'RE WEAK, YOU CANNOT BLOCK EVEN YOUR MOST PRIVATE THOUGHTS.

I'LL ONLY GIVE OUT BEJAIS WHEN I WANT TO.

YOU'LL NEVER HAVE ENOUGH ENERGY TO DISOBEY ME!

IN THE CAVE CITY, Z-KEE'S ALLIES ARE KIDNAPPED ONE BY ONE.

R-CHER'S HEADSTRONG. HE WANTS TO PROTECT HIS HOME.

Z-KEE KEEPS ON WORRYING.

HE THINKS I'M THE ENEMY BECAUSE I'M MOVING US TO BEJAIS ISLAND.

T-KWINIA?

MANY OTHERS HAVE REFUSED TO MOVE TO BEJAIS ISLAND. THEY'VE JOINED R-CHER!

WHAT? HOW CAN THAT BE?

I MUST GO! YOU KEEP SEARCHING FOR RUDY AND PENNY!

ONCE WE FIND RUDY ...

... WE'LL FIND EVERYONE ELSE.

NO WAY HAVE THEY ALL JOINED R-CHER. SOMETHING ELSE IS UP.

- 23 -

CONTROLLING THE HUMANS IS HOW HALYCRUSIANS WILL SURVIVE!

WE'RE JUST KIDS! YOU'RE MAKING US SOUND LIKE SUPERHEROES.

EVEN SO, WE HAVE PROGRESSED GREATLY SINCE YOU FOUND US.

HUMANS ARE THE KEY!

SUDDENLY ...

SCOTT WILL FIND A WAY TO RESCUE US!

PENNY COLLAPSES AGAINST THE WALL.

PENNY, CAN YOU HEAR ME? IT'S RUDY.

HAVE YOU GOT THE HANG OF THE MIND-READING?

I THINK SO. BUT MY HEAD REALLY HURTS. RUDY, WE'VE GOT TO GET OUT OF HERE!

R-CHER SUDDENLY PUSHES THROUGH THE GROUP OF KIDNAPPED HALYCRUSIANS.

HEY!

THUMP!

YOU AREN'T AS BRIGHT AS THE OTHERS. SCOTT DOESN'T EVEN KNOW YOU'RE HERE.

HE THINKS YOU'VE GONE BACK TO EARTH.

LEAVE THEM ALONE, R-CHER!

HA, HA, HA!

THUMP!

RUDY TRIES TO CHANNEL ANOTHER PRIVATE THOUGHT.

SCOTT AND AJ KNOW WE'RE HERE BECAUSE THEY HAVE THE PACKETS OF THE PORTAL MIXTURE.

THEY'RE LOOKING FOR US. I KNOW IT.

BUT R-CHER CAN HEAR EVERY WORD.

THUMP!

INTERESTING...

R-CHER, THERE'S NO MORE WOOD.

WHAT DO YOU MEAN "NO MORE"? THE HUMAN ONLY MADE FOUR TROLLEYS!

THUMP!

AND HE USED UP ALL THE WOOD.

I MUST FIND SCOTT. I'LL SEND HIM BACK TO EARTH FOR MORE WOOD.

LET THE HUMANS GO. WE CANNOT WORK TOGETHER IF THEY'RE IMPRISONED!

I CAN MAKE MORE TROLLEYS! BUT NOT LIKE THIS!

SUDDENLY PENNY GETS UP AND RUNS!

WHA—?

THUMP!

SCOTT! WE'RE IN HERE!

CATCH HER!

SCOTTY! WE'RE IN HERE! FOLLOW MY VOICE.

THUMP!

THUMP!

SCOTT!

SHE NEARLY ESCAPED!

MAKE SURE IT DOESN'T HAPPEN AGAIN!

MEANWHILE, ELSEWHERE IN THE CAVE CITY ...

SCOTT!

DID YOU HEAR THAT?

SO THAT'S WHERE THEY ARE!

TIME TO MAKE A PLAN ...

- 28 -

THE BOYS HAVE DECIDED TO LAY A TRAP.

I WONDER WHERE SCOTT IS?

I THINK IT'S SAFE TO FOLLOW NOW.

I'VE NEVER SEEN THAT ENTRY TUNNEL BEFORE.

WE WERE TOLD NOT TO BUILD THERE BECAUSE THE STONE IS WEAK.

IS IT SAFE?

NO! THERE ARE MOUNTAIN SWINE STOMPING RIGHT ABOVE THAT AREA!

WE'D BETTER PUT OUR PLAN INTO ACTION!

AJ HAS BEEN DRAGGED INTO R-CHER'S PRISON.

THUMP!

SO Z-KEE, WHAT'S HAPPENING?

MOMENTS LATER, T-KWINIA IS LED INTO THE CAVE DEN.

HAHA! WE'VE GOT T-KWINIA. SOON WE'LL HAVE SCOTT TOO. THEN WE'LL SEND HIM BACK TO EARTH FOR MORE SUPPLIES.

THUMP!

HE'LL DO AS WE SAY BECAUSE WE HAVE HIS SISTER IN CAPTIVITY!

NOW!

WHA—?

- 33 -

THE PRISONERS DIVE TO THE FLOOR.

THUMP!

GET UP! GET THEM UP!

GET UP PRISONERS! GET UP!

WHAT'S THAT NOISE?

SCREECH!

SCREECH!

WHAT IS IT R-CHER?

I ... I DON'T KNOW ...

SCOTT'S FRIENDS, THE SEA BIRDS, FLY DOWN THE TUNNEL.

ARGHHHH!

HELP!

ARGHHHH! WE'RE BEING ATTACKED!

OMPF, OUCH!

SCREECH!

KEEP RUNNING, PENNY! STAY WITH AJ AND RUDY!

THANKS, SCOTT!

GREAT JOB, SCOTT, AND NOT TOO SOON EITHER. LOOKS LIKE THIS CAVERN IS GOING TO COLLAPSE!

R-CHER WATCHES ON. HE IS FURIOUS.

IT'S NOT OVER YET, SCOTT!

YOU GO FIRST, Z-KEE! I WANT TO MAKE SURE THE SEA BIRDS GET OUT.

DON'T TAKE TOO LONG. IT'S NOT SAFE IN HERE!

THANKS FOR THE WARNING. I'LL SEE YOU OUTSIDE!

SCOTT SHOOS THE BIRDS BACK UP THE TUNNEL.

COME ON, BIRDIE, YOU DON'T WANT TO GET STUCK IN HERE!

I HAVEN'T SEEN R-CHER. I WONDER WHAT HAPPENED TO HIM? IT DOESN'T MATTER, TIME TO GET OUT!

- 39 -

WHERE DO YOU THINK YOU'RE GOING?

ARGH!

GET OFF ME, R-CHER!

OUTSIDE R-CHER'S DEN ...

WHERE'S SCOTT? HAS ANYONE SEEN HIM?

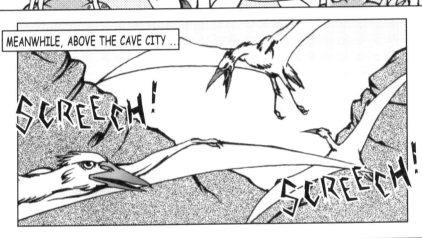

chapter 5 : The Cave Collapses!

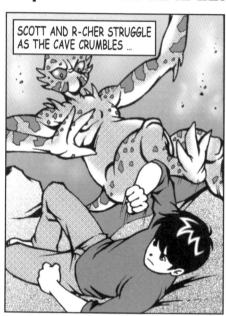

SCOTT AND R-CHER STRUGGLE AS THE CAVE CRUMBLES ...

I HAD THE PERFECT PLAN AND YOU RUINED IT!

R-CHER, LOOK OUT!

SCOTT'S DIVE SAVES R-CHER FROM BEING CRUSHED BY FALLING ROCKS.

SMACK

ARGH!

NO! DON'T YOU UNDERSTAND? WE'RE ALL HELPING EACH OTHER. YOU, ME, Z-KEE, T-KWINIA, RUDY, Q-STER, AJ!

WE ALL WORKED TOGETHER TO ESCAPE THE MOUNTAIN SWINE!

YOU KEPT GOING BACK TO EARTH AND LEAVING US WITH THE SWINE!

YOU CAN'T FORCE US TO STAY HERE. THIS ISN'T OUR WORLD, OUR HOME! YOU CAN'T ENSLAVE PEOPLE TO DO THINGS FOR YOU!

LOOK! IT'S THE HALYCRUSIANS WHO MOVED TO BEJAIS ISLAND!

ARE THEY HELPING SCOTT OR R-CHER?

NO ONE IS AGAINST EACH OTHER ON HALYCRUS. WELL, NO ONE SHOULD BE!

QUICK! WE MUST MOVE THESE ROCKS!

SCOTTY! WE'RE COMING!

Z-KEE!

WHERE ARE YOU GOING? WE HAVE TO SAVE SCOTT!

WE HAVE TO HELP Z-KEE. THE SWINE HAS GOT HIM!

SO? WHO CARES, AFTER WHAT THEY DID TO US?

PENNY, Z-KEE IS ON THE SAME SIDE AS US. WE ALL ARE.

SEE THOSE GUYS? THEY'RE FIGHTING TO SAVE SCOTT. AND THE WINGED TWO-HEADS AREN'T EVEN FROM EARTH OR HALYCRUS!

WAIT! I CAN SEE HIS TRAINER!

SCOTT! YOU'RE SAFE!

I'M OK.

BUDDY!

SCOTT! THANK GOODNESS!

SO YOU'RE ALL FREE. DON'T GLOAT. SOMEONE WILL COME TO GET ME.

WHAT ARE YOU DOING?

THEY'RE RESCUING YOU. A HALYCRUSIAN *AND* A HUMAN.

AS IT SHOULD BE.

T-KWINIA POINTS TO THE WINGED TWO-HEADS

SEE THEM UP THERE?

THEY'RE BATTLING THE SWINE SO WE COULD RESCUE BOTH OF YOU.

THEY DON'T HAVE ANY HELP. THEY ARE DOING IT ON THEIR OWN!

WE'RE DOING IT TOGETHER. WITH A LOT OF HELP FROM THE WINGED TWO-HEADS.

SO WE NEED EACH OTHER ...

EXACTLY. WE HAVE A NEW HOME, SAFE FROM OUR REAL FOE, THE SWINE.

SO WE WON'T NEED THE HUMANS FOR ANYTHING ...

... EXCEPT TO B[ ] FRIENDS. LIKE W[ ] ALWAYS WERE.